THE INSTITUTION OF CIVIL ENGINEERS

Construction research and development

VOL. 1. ORGANISATION AND FUNDING

Report of the ICE Research Sub-Committee
December 1986

 THOMAS TELFORD, LONDON

CONSTRUCTION RESEARCH AND DEVELOPMENT REPORTS

VOLUME 1. Organisation and funding.

VOLUME 2. Market sector priorities.

VOLUME 3. Background information to Volume 2. (Volume 3 has not been published and is lodged for reference in the Library of the Institution of Civil Engineers, 1-7 Great George Street, London SW1P 3AA. Telephone: 01-222 7722)

Published for The Institution of Civil Engineers by Thomas Telford Ltd, P.O. Box 101, 26-34 Old Street, London EC1P 1JH

First published 1986

ISBN 0 7277 0383 8

Typeset by Opus Magazines Ltd, London EC1

Printed in England by Imediaprint Ltd

ICE RESEARCH SUB-COMMITTEE

It is not always appreciated that the construction industry, in common with most others, is dependent upon innovation, research and development in order to meet increasingly stringent standards at home and to enable it to compete successfully abroad.

Further, in the construction industry particularly, the results of research need careful evaluation and validation and dissemination in forms usable by practising engineers, if maximum benefit is to be obtained from investment in R&D.

There are many competent research organisations in the field of construction but they are predominantly supported by public sector funding. The Institution of Civil Engineers believes that the industry itself should become more involved in the selection and funding of research and in its implementation, and that to achieve the best results it is essential to establish a national co-ordinating body which would recognise the partnership between the industry, the public sector including Government, and the research organisations themselves.

The Institution has always considered research to be an important interest. It played a principal role in establishing CIRIA and made a major contribution to the Task Force Report in 1981. It now proposes to establish a permanent Research Sub-Committee and offers its assistance in helping to establish research priorities. This will not, however, be enough. It looks to Government to establish the framework within which research investment in construction can become more rewarding to both client and the industry and more beneficial to the nation.

D.A.D. Reeve
ICE President, 1985-86
4 November 1986

ICE RESEARCH SUB-COMMITTEE MEMBERS

F.G.E. Irwin, BA, BAI, MSc, FICE, FIStructE (*Chairman*)
Member of Council
Engineering Committee
Director, Ove Arup & Partners

L.S. Blake, BSc(Eng), PhD, FICE, FIStructE
Consultant
(Director of CIRIA until April 1986)

D.I. Blockley, BEng, PhD, MICE, FIStructE
Engineering Management Group Board
Reader in Civil Engineering
University of Bristol

J. Campbell, MCIBSE
CIBSE representative
Technical Director, Ove Arup & Partners

R. Clare, BSc, DIC, FICE, MIHT
Head of Projects Development Department
Sir Robert McAlpine & Sons Limited

I.F. Christie, BSc, PhD, FICE, FIPHE, MIWES
Ground Engineering Group Board
Senior Lecturer, University of Edinburgh

J.B.L. Faulkner, BSc, FICE
Director, W.S. Atkins Group Consultants

H.B. Gould, FICE, FIStructE
Member of Council
Structural Engineering Group Board
Consultant, G. Maunsell & Partners

G.M. Gray, MSc(Eng), DIC, FICE, FIStructE
Water Engineering Group Board
Manager
Building and Civil Engineering Division
CIRIA

J.C. Judson, BSc(Eng), ACGI, FICE, MIME
Energy Engineering Group Board
Chairman, W.S. Atkins Group Consultants

A.D. May, MA, MICE, MIHT, FCIT
Transportation Engineering Group Board
Professor of Transport Engineering
Institute for Transport Studies
University of Leeds

G. Somerville, BSc, PhD, FEng, FICE, FIStructE, FIHT, FACI
Director, Research & Technical Services
Cement & Concrete Association

M.F.C. Thorn, MA, MS, MICE
Maritime Engineering Group Board
Head, Tidal Engineering Dept
Hydraulics Research, Wallingford

R.P. Thorogood, BSc, PhD
Co-ordinator for Civil Engineering Research
Department of the Environment and the SERC

Secretariat

David Wallace
Director, Learned Society, ICE

Nadia Ellis
Engineering Services, ICE

CONTENTS

PRINCIPAL FINDINGS

1. Research, development and dissemination require increased investment if the construction industry is to survive in overseas markets and to meet the increasingly stringent demands of clients in the UK for durable, functional and cost efficient products at home. The study of market sectors in Volume 2 of this report has produced a formidable list of high priority R&D requirements.

    There is ample evidence of the very high costs and social effects of failing to undertake sufficient R&D and dissemination in matters such as concrete durability and in several areas of the housing field.

2. There is a vital need for a co-ordinating body for both civil engineering and building research as recommended in the Task Force Report in 1981 and the 1985 NEDO 'Strategy for Construction R&D' Report. This should be an umbrella organisation to all existing research groups promoting co-ordination, industry participation, establishment of research priorities and dissemination. In addition, the SERC should be encouraged to increase the status and funding of its construction related research activities.

3. Too often research results are not put to use because no one is responsible for ensuring that successful work is developed, validated and disseminated in a form that is usable by practitioners. This is a major problem which delays more immediate returns on research investment. Budgets for selected research projects should cover all stages of the research process, including management, validation and presentation of the information in a form usable by the industry.

4. Research and Development funding amounts to 0.65% of construction output, which is less than for other major industries and less than many of our major overseas competitors. A substantial increase is needed to fund increased R&D and improved dissemination.

5. Contractors and consultants are, typically, agents who provide a service based on progress payments and who do not own and sell the product. Consequently, their ability to contribute to research is small in relation to the turnover of the industry and its research needs. In addition, private clients do not recognise the need to contribute to research. Consequently, apart from manufacturers, most research is funded by the public sector.

6. A levy on all construction to fund research is likely to be unpopular and too complex administratively as a method of raising funds. Increased participation by industry in the selection of research, and the formation of collaborative clubs would have many benefits including an increased contribution by industry. However, the public sector including Government are the client for 80% of civil

engineering and 50% of all construction and must remain the principal contributors to research.

7. The Government should recognise the need for a substantial research capability if the industry is to be efficient at home and to compete abroad. It should take the initiative to ensure that the necessary money is made available. A portion of the funds could be raised from clients and the industry through collaborative programmes.

8. The Institution of Civil Engineers should establish a permanent Research Sub-Committee to promote research in support of industry and monitor its progress. Given increased funding, the Institution through its Engineering Group Boards and associated societies could help the existing research organisations and the proposed co-ordinating body to identify research priorities and promote dissemination.

1. INTRODUCTION

The Research Sub-Committee was initiated by the ICE Engineering Committee and it commenced its work in September 1985. Its terms of reference are:

(i)   to review the Task Force Report in respect of new user requirements and new technologies which have arisen during the past five years

(ii)   to comment on the NEDO Report when published

(iii)   to examine the adequacy of funding arrangements for civil engineering research and make recommendations on methods which would improve the present situation

(iv)   to encourage the dissemination of information and application of results of research in a structured way

(v)   to support the publication and distribution of 'Research Focus'

(vi)   to encourage the dissemination of the results of research through the holding of specialist conferences, articles in 'New Civil Engineer' etc

(vii)   to report on the Sub-Committee's future role after 12 months, with recommendations for the future organisation of the Institution's research interests.

In addition, the Sub-Committee was asked to respond to the questions on research posed by the House of Lords Select Committee on Science and Technology, Sub-Committee 1 – Civil R&D. The responses to the House of Lords and the NEDO Report 'Strategy for Construction R&D' were both completed and issued in March 1986. These reports are lodged in the Institution library.

The Research Sub-Committee was formed of representatives of the Institution's Engineering Group Boards, together with members of other organisations who were co-opted so as to create a forum representing academia, contractors, consultants and research organisations with interests covering all the market sectors in civil engineering and the engineering of buildings.

Links were established with research associations and Government bodies involved in research as noted in the Acknowledgements, but in most cases formal exchange of information proved unnecessary because of the informal connections of sub-committee members with these bodies. In addition, some individual members of the Institution contributed opinions.

The Chairman and two members of the NEDO Research Strategy Committee made a presentation to the Sub-Committee on their findings which, in addition to their report, was extremely helpful to the work of the Sub-Committee.

This report is a development built on the Task Force Report 'Long-Term Research and Development Requirements in Civil Engineering,' published in 1981, and the Sub-Committee acknowledges the formidable contribution of that report to research and development objectives and in providing a substantial framework and reservoir of information for the Sub-Committee's tasks.

In order to examine funding and dissemination of R&D, the Sub-Committee found it necessary to examine the organisation of research and reports on this aspect as an essential part of the total picture.

There are many definitions of Research and Development which vary greatly in their breadth. The Sub-Committee considers that R&D is an integral part of good construction and should permeate concept, design, construction and maintenance. It has therefore adopted the definition given by Dr L. Blake in his 1986 Unwin lecture, namely, 'the endeavour to discover new or to collate old facts by scientific study of a subject,' and it becomes effective when it is carefully selected, studied, developed, tested, disseminated and taught.

The Task Force had thirty-nine papers prepared on Product (Market) Areas and twenty-eight papers prepared on Discipline (Technology) Areas. All of these papers were reviewed, wherever possible, by the original authors, and otherwise by new reviewers. Some new papers were prepared and a number of the reviews were substantial papers in their own right. The assistance of all these contributors is gratefully acknowledged.

In order to distill the findings from these papers, they were grouped into market sectors corresponding to the appropriate Institution Group Board and the Group Board representatives, together with their Boards, have provided an analysis of the present needs in their market sectors.

The Sub-Committee's findings and the review of research needs have been assembled in three volumes:

Volume 1.   Organisation and funding
Volume 2.   Market sector priorities
Volume 3.   Background information to Volume 2

Volume 3 has not been reproduced on account of its size but is lodged in the Institution library for reference purposes, and individual papers can be obtained from there.

The Chairman is indebted to the members of the Sub-Committee and to all who prepared special papers for their hard work and co-operation, and to the Institution Secretariat for their work in administration and assembly of the report.

2. PROGRESS SINCE 1981 TASK FORCE REPORT

2.1. Preface

The Civil Engineering Task Force Report was commissioned jointly by the Departments of the Environment and of Transport and the Science and Engineering Research Council to review the long-term needs for R&D in civil engineering, for a period of up to 20 years ahead.

The Task Force attempted to predict the changing demands for civil engineering work (in nature and extent in relation to need) encompassing work in the UK and that by British firms overseas. It made recommendations on priority areas for innovation and the consequent needs for R&D; it made recommendations on priorities in R&D; and it proposed an organisational system for continuing the development and monitoring of the forward needs for R&D in civil engineering.

Although limited by its terms of reference to civil engineering aspects of R&D, the Task Force found it impossible to exclude all other sectors of construction and, therefore, many of its recommendations were applicable to building. In particular, the recommendations on the required organisational systems were considered to apply to construction as a whole.

It would be surprising if the predictions of demand for civil engineering work and recommended priorities for R&D made by the Task Force in 1981 did not now require some modification in the light of more recent information and events. For this reason, the Institution of Civil Engineers has instituted a review of the 70 reports by authorities in the areas of technology and civil engineering 'products' on which the Task Force was based. A similar review is being undertaken by the Institution of Structural Engineers on structural engineering aspects of the Report.

The purpose of this Chapter is to indicate the progress that has been made in the past five years towards achieving the objectives put forward in the Task Force's recommendations.

2.2. Priorities in R&D

There are some clear indications that research programmes of organisations in both the private and public sectors have been influenced by the Task Force's recommendations on priorities. However, the extent to which Government Research Establishments have been able to respond has been severely limited by staffing reductions and commitments to work required by Government Departments in connection with their statutory responsibilities, including regulations and dealing with urgent problems such as with large panel structures and reinforcement corrosion.

Response from the private sector research organisations has also been limited primarily by lack of finance. R&D departments of contractors, for example, have been severely reduced as a result of the continuing recession in construction. Financial support to the Research Associations, such as CIRIA, remains inadequate from both public and private sectors to provide the significant changes in priority that the Task Force have sought.

The most marked response to the Task Force Report recommendations came from the Science and Engineering Research Council's decision to establish an enhanced programme of civil engineering research at the Universities and Polytechnics. This programme, currently financed to the extent of about £3 million per annum, was started in 1983 with emphasis on research into performance in the field and at large scale, and on research to stimulate innovation and developments. Four major subject areas were selected, each with a co-ordinator to develop programmes in:

- structural engineering (including earthquake engineering and demolition)
- hydraulics, pollution control and public health engineering
- geotechnics
- repair, maintenance and operation.

Important new facilities have been established to support the programme with a wide flume flood channel (SERC and HRL shared the cost). A shaking table at Bristol, capable of simulating earthquakes, and approval have been given to establish a national test bed site on soft clay, required for a wide variety of geotechnical research projects.

The SERC programme has received substantial assistance in the form of practical help, advice and finance from most of the public and private sector research organisations, particularly HRL, WRc, BRE, TRRL and CIRIA. It is guided by a sub-committee comprising four academics and four industry representatives — all members of the Institution of Civil Engineers. The Construction Industry Directorate of the DoE has appointed a senior member of its staff to assist in the SERC programme.

The SERC initiative is now beginning to produce useful results, and there seems ample justification for an expansion in funding, bearing in mind the importance of the programme and that present total expenditure by the SERC in civil engineering research amounts to less than 3% of its annual budget. The reduction in grants by the UGC has, to some extent, reduced the benefit of enhanced SERC funding to academia.

In addition to the SERC initiative, there are some examples of positive progress by others in furthering the Task Force's recommendations.

Research in support of British firms working overseas
This includes work by CIRIA, BRE and others on the problems of concrete construction in the Middle East, and the recent CIRIA survey commissioned by the DoE to establish the support required and how best to provide it.

Development of site investigation techniques
Work by BRE, TRRL and CIRIA is continuing on this subject, and includes a joint effort to improve contractual arrangements for site investigation.

Performance data on systems for coastal protection
This includes a continuing programme of work by HRL and CIRIA, funded by MAFF, and the Institution's Coastal Engineering Research Panel's assessment of priorities in this field.

Development of improved methods of construction
Civil engineering requirements are to be included in the DTI's programme on the application of advanced robotics (contracts to CIRIA).

Processes for building on poor ground
High priority is being given to this subject in the programmes of BRE and CIRIA.

Repair, maintenance, replacement and refurbishment
This includes work by the WRc and others in developing 'no-dig' methods of sewer replacement, and CIRIA's guide on refurbishment, etc.

Production of authoritative reviews and guidance
In addition to CIRIA's continuing programme in this field, there has been a recognition by other research and professional bodies of the need for more effective technology transfer overall.

Management
The work of the SERC's SPP, although primarily concerned with building, is relevant. CIRIA's investigations into and reports on a variety of alternative forms of contract, including that for tunnelling work, are also in line with the Task Force's recommendations.

2.3.	**Organisation and funding of R&D**	

The Task Force concluded that there was a need for better co-ordination of research funded through the various bodies, with the professional 'users' of research playing a dominant role in specifying research objectives. It criticised the system developed within the DoE and DTp as restricting the ability of the Research Associations and the Government Research Establishments to assist industry, and also as excluding the needs of direct 'customers', such as the local and public authorities, and the industrial and professional 'users'. It also drew attention to the need to increase the relevance of research to practice — for example, by the more effective involvement of those in practice in all stages of the research process, in the manner adopted by CIRIA.

One of the most important recommendations by the Task Force was for the appointment of a Board to advise the Secretaries of State for the Environment and for Transport on the objectives, priorities and balance of R&D programmes to support construction for all purposes. This, the Secretaries of State declined to do; instead, they asked the Building and Civil Engineering EDCs to advise on the annual allocation of R&D funds in support of the industry and also to recommend an overall strategy for R&D. The EDCs appointed the Research Strategy Committee in 1982 to undertake these tasks and the Committee reported in 1985. The Research Strategy Committee's principal recommendation was for a Board to be established to improve the co-ordination of research nationally and to carry out other duties closely resembling those recommended by the Task Force four years earlier.

It must be said that during the past five years there has been little improvement in the organisation and funding of construction R&D. Similarly, there has been little improvement in the system in respect of including the needs of direct 'customers' in programme decisions or in securing more effective involvement of those in practice in all stages of the research process. The recent establishment of a Joint Research Group, enabling local authorities to discuss research needs with Government Departments, is a welcome step forward. However, it is to be hoped that the two Secretaries of State most concerned will now accept the recommendations of the Task Force and Research Strategy Committees in respect of organisation.

Funding arrangements for construction R&D have become more complex during the past five years principally by lack of co-ordination between the nine Government Departments funding construction research for their own needs. A further complication is the competition for private sector funds between Government Research Establishments, the SERC, academia and the Research Associations such as CIRIA. Such competition is wasteful of manpower in Government establishments and weakens the well established mechanism for collaborative, private and public funding and work through the Research Associations.

2.4.	**The consequences of neglect**

During the past five years, public sector funding has decreased in real terms with substantial reductions particularly at BRE and TRRL. A similar reduction has been seen in the private sector attributable to the continuing recession in construction and, in the case of contractors, by the increase in sub-contracting and labour-only work.

The Task Force Report pointed out that R&D in civil engineering 'must include a stable core of fundamental and forward-looking research and provide the necessary interaction between research workers and practitioners at all levels and stages of design and construction process'.

The concentration on immediate problems forced on the R&D community, exacerbated by the reduction in expenditure by public and private sectors alike, has resulted in a very serious reduction in the essential core of fundamental and forward-looking research. The loss of this essential core will have a significant effect on the national R&D capability for many years to come. It takes several years to develop experienced and effective research teams.

Another result of neglect during the past five years has been a reduction in the national capability to innovate and develop new methods of construction. The Task Force Report and, more recently, the NEDO Report have strongly recommended action by Government, as the principal client for construction, to facilitate and provide funds for appropriate experimental and development work in connection with specific Government projects. Without development and innovation, the British industry must inevitably fall behind its competitors in Europe, America and the Far East.

3.   THE VALUE OF RESEARCH AND DEVELOPMENT

3.1   Preface

British civil engineering has gained an international recognition that brings substantial overseas earnings to the UK. To maintain its international competitiveness and success, the civil engineering industry must continually advance the technological base on which it depends. Many of the industry's main international competitors from the western world – France, Germany, Holland, Denmark – benefit from very substantial government investment in research and development. In Japan, where the structure of the industry differs greatly from Western Europe, formidable resources are being deployed in civil engineering research.

Civil engineering is a technology based industry, and the associated building industry is rapidly becoming so as craft based traditions diminish.

New or changed materials continually emerge, as do new types of plant and equipment, which alter methods of construction. The sources and type of naturally occurring material alter as existing supplies become exhausted. The nature of sites changes on account of the increased use of locations that have been the scene of previous constructions. In some market sectors, an increasing amount of maintenance and repair work is becoming necessary as works from the Victorian period up to post-war construction need either modernising or reconstruction. Overseas, the construction industry market shifts periodically to countries where the climate, materials and labour differ from previous experience.

This scene of constant change demands an effective research and development industry which is constantly providing the practitioner with developed and proven knowledge so that he can use the scarce capital resources for construction to provide functional, durable and economic artefacts. Besides the R&D effort needed to cope with change, research is also needed to test and establish innovative ideas from within the industry and to foster basic research. Competition in overseas markets is so intense that it is only through the efficiency of better methods and the reputation deriving from durable products that the UK industry will continue to find markets overseas.

3.2   Assessment of value

In view of the exploratory nature of any research project, it is not possible to quantify the value that will derive from it in advance of its being carried out. Decisions on particular investments should result, through the consultative processes described in other chapters, from the pool of proposals from the market sectors. Clearly, resources cannot be made available to tackle all projects, but the amount spent on the research process as a whole should be established as a percentage of total turnover that is comparable with other industries and with construction research expenditure in our major competitor countries.

It is possible that some of the major advances in civil engineering practice could have taken place without an associated programme of supportive research — by trial and error, in fact, which was the process adopted in construction throughout history, and practically until the 18th century. Such a process, with the risks and higher costs that it is likely to entail, is unacceptable today. Future advances in civil engineering practice are dependent on research. In some cases, innovations occur as a result of a research 'push' or, probably more frequently, as a result of a practitioner 'pull'; both require interaction between research and practice. The Task Force Report drew attention to the value of the technical (research) expert in this respect.

A number of major problems are being faced today, because of the ageing infrastructure, because of unexpected loading conditions or because materials and components have failed to perform as anticipated. It is possible that reasonable solutions to these problems could be evolved without supportive research, but only at very high cost, including the unnecessary demolition of some structures attacked, for example, by HAC or steel corrosion. With a potential annual cost in the UK for maintenance, repair or renewal of such civil engineering structures and works in the UK in the order of £1 billion, there can be little doubt that increased expenditure on civil engineering R&D would be amply repaid by the level of savings it would ensure.

In support of this claim, mention must be made of the following: the techniques developed for sewer and pipeline replacement; the criteria established and instrumentation developed for the assessment of structural adequacy; hydraulic modelling techniques; geotechnical investigation instrumentation; together with the development of reliable theory and analytical methods for practical use.

There have been various attempts to quantify the value of R&D and to apply cost-benefit analysis to the selection of R&D projects. It is even more difficult to do this for R&D than it is to quantify and apply cost-benefit analysis to engineering projects. In its 25th Anniversary publication (1985), CIRIA assessed the cost benefit of its total programme as being well in excess of ten times expenditure, with individual cases providing an annual benefit in excess of thirty times the cost of the research. R.S. Taylor (1985) assesses the benefit of R&D by a contractor's firm to be in excess of an order of magnitude of the cost.

There is no doubt that misdirected research can waste money, but the systems that exist for the selection and financing of research ensure that little or no research is wasteful, although the degree of benefit does vary from organisation to organisation.

In his 1960 Unwin lecture, Lord Baker said that all civil engineers, except those engaged in the most hackneyed of work, are engaged in a careful search and enquiry (for information) — which is one definition of research. It must be emphasised that, without an effective core of national research, the source of information which practitioners need would be severely depleted and of doubtful reliability.

3.3. Examples

Some examples of research which have been of great benefit, and others where insufficient investigation has led to expensive problems, are listed below as a demonstration of the need for properly assessed research expenditure.

Some examples of beneficial research are:

- Theoretical research into the method of slices for the analysis of slopes permitted the use of steeper slopes for the same factor of safety. Substantial savings have resulted.

- Improved theories allowing for ground/structure interaction have reduced the cost of many raft and piled raft foundations.

- Current design and rehabilitation of urban drainage have been greatly facilitated through research and development.

- Construction of tall buildings on London clay has been made possible through research and development.

- PFA and blast furnace slag, which were valueless materials, have been found uses through the application of research.

- Wind loading: architectural developments in recent years have produced a proliferation of building shapes that are very susceptible to wind damage. The work that has been done, resulting in changes to the Codes of Practice, has prevented the loss of integrity of very many buildings.

- Concrete constituents: the work of BRE has resulted in the banning of the use of chlorides, now known to be very damaging but previously thought only to have advantages. Again, the work resulted in changes to the Codes of Practice.

- Wall ties: for many years, it had been thought that galvanised wall ties would outlast the brickwork in which they were incorporated. The research work has demonstrated the inaccuracy of this belief and has resulted in radical changes in specification.

- Plastic theory of structures.

- Finite element analysis, which is now extensively used.

- Development of welding technology.

The CIRIA publication (1985) gives some sixty examples of the benefits of R&D to civil engineering practice during the past 25 years and, of these, mentions the following as the top areas of activities within its own field:

- the design and construction of formwork and falsework for concrete
- foundations and piling
- bills of quantities and forms of contract
- structural design, including guides and work on loading, safety and limit state design
- safety in construction, including compressed air, working, trenching, use of chemicals
- offshore structures in steel and concrete
- diving and underwater working

Other areas worthy of mention are:

- wind engineering
- concrete bridge deck design — especially for motorway programme
- nuclear pressure vessels

Some examples of insufficient R&D:

- The problems of glass reinforced cement might have been avoided by more development and test applications.

- Precast housing: more development could have avoided current problems of substantial magnitude.

- Precast multi-storey flats: the use of continental systems without sufficient investigation of their application in the UK has led to the elimination of a potentially satisfactory method of construction.

- Shrinkable clays: work done in the decades before the drought of 1976 did not prevent many of the foundation problems — because the building industry, through insufficient dissemination and education, did not apply the findings. However, useful advice was given for remedial work and later for new structures.

4. SELECTION AND IMPLEMENTATION OF RESEARCH PROJECTS

4.1.   Preface

Completing a research project and writing a report giving the results are both comparatively straightforward processes. Identifying priorities in what research should be done, funding and organising it, and then taking the results through into effective use in practice are much more complex procedures. Recognition of the steps involved in this total process is essential, if the latter is to be done well.

In all the market sectors of civil engineering, research must be closely related to practice. In deriving a strategy for the selection and use of R&D, it is therefore important to identify the essential elements which make up practice, i.e. to keep clearly in mind the overall problem that awaits the results from R&D. This is especially relevant in maintaining an overall balance of research, i.e. in ensuring that all parts of the problem, represented by practice, are being treated to the same extent.

Knowledge obtained from research is in itself insufficient, if the means do not exist effectively to use that knowledge in practice. Practice may have to adapt or change, as new knowledge becomes available. This requires two-way communication between research and practice, often accompanied by essential development work.

A review of present practice reveals a general lack of awareness of these issues. This must change, if a proper strategy for the selection and use of R&D is to be developed for the construction industry.

4.2.   Selection and use R&D

The process of selecting appropriate research areas, defining and funding projects and making effective use of the results within the industry, requires a series of steps of which research itself is but one single action.

The entire process of examining a research problem through to its successful resolution has been identified as requiring eight steps. These are as follows:

– Discussion of need between industry and researchers in conjunction with a co-ordinating body

– Options for funding after a review of existing information in the UK and abroad

– Research

– Development

– Demonstration projects

– Structured information

– Dissemination

– Training

This eight-step process should be promoted throughout the industry; it should also be monitored by any research-initiating body — and by industry itself — to ensure that the process is completed whenever a research project indicates useful benefits. Research managers would be needed to bring projects through the stages to completion. At present, no-one is responsible for this process.

The cost of the process is likely to exceed the cost of the research step by several orders of magnitude. Without it, good research may not be fully utilised; perhaps, worse, research results may be used out of context or not translated properly into practice.

If the process were introduced, the possible budget costs of proposals would increase above present perceived costs of research even though only a proportion of projects may survive the reviews that would be needed at each state. However, the concept seems essential if the industry is to move towards the twenty-first century in a healthy and technologically advanced state.

The implementation of these steps as a general procedure would require promotion and support by a co-ordinating body.

4.3. Achieving balance in research

After defining a priority area of research, there is a need for a balanced approach to the problem. There are basic sets of criteria which have to be in harmony with one another if the successful performance of every civil engineering artefact is to be achieved. A typical list of such elements is:

  (i)   design demands and capacities
  (ii)   performance criteria
  (iii)   safety factors and margins
  (iv)   design models and procedures
  (v)   material specifications
  (vi)   minimum standards of construction
  (vii)   acceptable levels of maintenance.

It is essential that the state of knowledge of each of these sets of criteria is recognised, and emphasis in R&D given to those elements which are lagging behind the others; the sets are interdependent, and failure of any one can lead to the failure of the whole. They are not an expression of R&D needs in any market sector, but their existence should be borne in mind when defining needs and setting priorities.

It is of crucial importance to develop a strategy which maintains a satisfactory knowledge base for each set, thus ensuring a proper balance. The nature and make-up of the criteria and their balance will vary in different market sectors within the civil engineering industry. However, recognition of their interdependence will help in making judgements on priorities.

There are numerous bodies in the construction industry, both in practice and in academe, which contribute at present to the research effort. Each has its own motivation, and will contribute to one or more of the sets of criteria in different ways. However, in any field of application, it is quite common to find that the research effort is distributed disproportionately between the elements. Typically, most research projects relate to design models and to materials specifications, with very little on workmanship standards. Additionally, there is a lack of consistency in deriving safety factors and margins, while translating the research data into a form appropriate to actual conditions in practice. These remarks obtain particularly to the building and structural sectors, but can also be related to other civil engineering applications.

Apart from the inconsistencies mentioned above, there is a potentially more serious problem. Design demands, performance and maintenance levels are often ignored in research terms. This leads to a lack of balance, which is becoming a more serious issue as designs continue to be 'refined' by way of the other criteria. There can be strong commercial motivation for more refined or productive construction methods, but the greater overall priority in R&D terms may lie in the better definition of performance requirements (e.g. life-cycle costing of roads and bridges; design life of nuclear plants; thermal and acoustic standards in buildings).

Current performance criteria have evolved historically, and there is no proper rationale behind them, to permit extrapolation into the future. By suggesting that considerably more work is required on this element, we are suggesting, in effect, that research needs to be done to define the real questions properly, which must be addressed by research on the other elements. Failure to do this means that immaculate answers can be produced to the wrong questions. A further advantage, in tackling this element properly, would be the definition of performance standards against which innovations (in materials, design or construction methods) could be properly measured. This would be of benefit to those engaged in industrial research, in clearly establishing a series of well-defined targets. One particular factor deserves special mention – durability and design life. Associated with this is the establishment of minimum levels of maintenance which relate to the normal design life and which are consistent with other criteria.

5. DEVELOPMENT WORK

5.1. Preface

Research and development is often responsive in nature, within an on-going industry, which is subject to change both in its make-up and in its practices. Generally, this change is of the 'incremental improvement' type, which can usually be detected and due compensation made. However, surges in the demands made on the construction industry can occur, often requiring research which is 'substantially innovative' in character. Here, it is equally important to ensure that a full development programme is initiated and that it is monitored throughout all its stages.

5.2. Need for development

The application of new or 'improved' techniques or materials on a widespread scale without an exhaustive development programme puts at risk scarce capital resources. It also risks bringing such innovations into disrepute through applying changes without fully resolving the inevitable teething problems. Even worse, the innovation can, if it has not been tested in the context of prevailing workmanship and other standards, lead to failure of the artefact to perform the function for which it was intended.

5.3 Demonstration projects

Demonstration projects are also an important part of the proving process, and major clients with large rolling programmes of work need to be encouraged to undertake a share of this necessary stage in innovation. This can be achieved if researchers and practitioners can be brought together as part of a continuing dialogue on the problems to be solved and the benefits to be gained in turning research into a workable reality.

The civil engineering industry covers a very wide range of activities whose needs can vary widely. It is possible, for example, to carry out research in a range of materials and to apply the results successfully to one market sector, e.g. building. Transferring that information into other sectors, such as bridges, or ports and harbours, requires care since loads and performance requirements are different. On the other hand, experience gained by a major thrust in one sector is often not fed back into other sectors, e.g. the R&D and innovation involved in North Sea oil production platforms could have been put to greater use for a range of land-based structures.

5.4. Examples of insufficient development

Examples from the post-war years, where the two factors of research and development were perhaps forced out of step, might include:

- durability of concrete structures
- box girder bridges
- industrialised building in the 1960s
- prefabricated reinforced concrete housing.

Some of these examples emphasise the point regarding the need for development work.

Firstly, consider durability, and the corrosion of reinforcement in concrete in particular. Research has shown that preventing corrosion depends primarily on achieving low permeability in the concrete; it has also identified the factors which influence permeability, and has largely quantified these, thus leading to the derivation of a proper 'specification'. There remains the problem of ensuring that this specification is met. In simple terms, there is no practical, generally accepted, method for directly measuring either permeability or the major factors which influence this (e.g. cement content, water/cement ratio, compaction, curing); instead, reliance has to be placed on the largely meaningless (in this context) standard cube test. This is an example of where the results from research have not been properly applied, owing to the necessary development work of producing complementary tests being neglected.

Secondly, there were steel box girder bridges. Developments in analytical and design methods (usually computer based) permitted economic solutions to be produced for many bridges. However, this was not always matched by developments in construction practice — in producing plates flat enough to meet the design assumptions, or in coping with the tolerances involved on site. This is an example of lack of development work; it is also an example of a lack of balance between the various elements in the package described above.

Finally, there was industrialised building. In theory, a satisfactory specification did exist, based substantially on experience in Europe. In practice, the tolerances involved, and the standards of workmanship required, were not achieved on site in the UK. In effect, the concept was imported from Europe, without full consideration of suitability, social and climatic conditions, or of the required technical backup or the quality of supervision available.

The preceding examples illustrate the type of development work being called for in this report, which, if it is to be successful in practice, requires two-way communication between the researcher and the practitioner — to ensure that research findings are accompanied by developments in appropriate practical technology. Development work will come in different guises in different applications in different market sectors; what is constant is the need for it, in effectively bridging the gap between research and practice.

6. DISSEMINATION OF RESEARCH RESULTS

6.1. Preface

It is a common complaint, and a common experience, that research results are not readily available to practising engineers, and are thus not being effectively applied and exploited by the civil engineering industry. As the breadth of scientific discipline, including environmental sciences, relevant to present-day engineering projects increases, this problem is growing. The present means of dissemination of research are unstructured and haphazard. This causes waste, in that good research is not being translated into engineering practice because engineers either do not know about it or do not understand it. There is an urgent need to make recent research results accessible to the engineering industry in a form that is at once comprehensible and relevant, and in which certainties are clearly stated. This requires effort in partnership between the industry and the researchers, from which both would gain. Industry would become technologically more advanced, and thus more competitive; the researchers would be able more clearly to identify research needs and, therefore, likely sources of support for research. Effective dissemination of research should be a matter of mutual interest.

6.2. Original research

The first step in the dissemination of information from research is that a project is written up in some way and the results published, often in the form of scientific theses, consigned to the archives of university libraries, or as specialist papers in scientific journals. In either form they are generally inaccessible or unintelligible to the practising engineer. The busy practitioner has a problem both in being aware of this information and, more important, in having the time and expertise to judge whether or not the information can be directly applied in his day-to-day practice. In effect, the raw research represented by these scientific and engineering research papers needs reworking, to permit proper integration into the commonwealth of existing practices.

Researchers are appointed primarily on scientific merit, not on ability to communicate, and it is unrealistic to expect a good researcher necessarily to be a good communicator. The role of the researcher is to provide intellectual insight, and to carry out experiment or analysis that will advance understanding of the physical world, and thereby advance the state of the art of engineering. The interpretation and dissemination of these research results is a skill in itself, and is a task which may need to be delegated to a suitably qualified engineering 'interpreter' and writer. The researcher will naturally endeavour to conserve his budget for his research activity, and will be parsimonious in providing for general dissemination of the results. An adequate and separately ear-marked allocation of resources needs to be made specifically for this purpose by the funders of research. This should be free to be allocated to whatever organisation is best able to interpret and publicise the research to the user industry.

6.3. Research reviews

In many subject areas there is an enormous international store of published and unpublished research data and analysis, scattered through research institutes and a wide variety of journals and conference proceedings. Much of it is not indexed in national and international catalogues. To bring this together, to validate, rework and normalise the data as necessary, to present a coherent and homogeneous statement of present knowledge, and to interpret it in terms of practical application is a task as demanding and as worthwhile as any piece of practical experimentation. Much effective and practical research can be done in libraries, but such work is not considered to be an intellectually respectable activity in its own right, and many scientific journals are reluctant or unwilling to accept review papers for publication. Yet it is precisely this form of dissemination of research results that is of value to the practising engineer.

A change of attitude is required on the part of the funders, examiners and publishers of research to allow such application-orientated research to take place. Research funders should accept and encourage projects that review, collate and interpret existing research results, and such projects should be awarded funds and status on a par with practical experimental projects. It would not be unrealistic to spend up to 20% of the available research budget for this purpose, which is potentially very cost-effective. The professional engineering journals, including ICE Proceedings, should be pressed to accept such papers as meritorious. The Institutions could further promote this constructive attitude towards the practical interpretation of research to the profession by offering awards to recognise those who serve the engineering profession in this way.

6.4. Publication and meetings

A great deal of research information is published through the twin media of technical journals and conference proceedings, not all of which operate a strict vetting procedure. Most journals and proceedings fall into two basic categories: those publishing only research papers and probably read only by researchers; and those publishing papers on engineering practice and projects, probably read only by practitioners. Inevitably, this leads to very poor communication between research and practice because neither side knows or asks, 'What is the present level of knowledge in this field?' The proliferation of scientific and technical journals, meetings and conferences is a growing problem for researcher and practitioner alike, and has the effect of recycling undigested material. Although a majority of published research is in English, worthwhile papers have always also been published in French and German, and now some good papers are published in Russian, Japanese and Chinese.

Publication in print, which adequately served the needs of the nineteenth century, has long since ceased to be an assuredly effective means of disseminating research results to either the world of research or the world of engineering practice. The field of print is too fragmented and diffuse to be a reliable source of information. In some narrow disciplines, Abstracting Journals perform an effective service in reviewing and summarising a very wide spectrum of publications. To be successful, an abstracting journal needs a sound indexed framework of relevant key words, and informative abstracts that allow the content of each entry to be fully appraised. Excellent examples can be seen in 'Applied Mechanics Reviews' (American Society of Mechanical Engineers) and 'Selected Water Resources Abstracts' (US Dept of the Interior). Well-indexed and cross-referenced journals of this kind are to be encouraged in specialist fields, but they are expensive to do well and unlikely to be commercially self-financing. While they assist the quest for information by the diligent enquirer, they do not disseminate results and information to the engineering practitioner.

To bring order to the chaos of printed publications, the civil engineering profession needs to concentrate publication of research results in a select range of refereed journals. Journals that are read by practitioners and written for by academics (e.g. 'Traffic Engineering and Control') should be identified and fostered. The Institution of Civil Engineers should consider how it might promote this through its own publications: for example, it might seek to reprint meritorious papers, and translations of foreign-language papers, perhaps in a special journal. These recommendations logically identify a strong need for the Institution to undertake a radical review of its existing range of publications, and to consider how it can best be reshaped to meet the needs of the end of the twentieth century.

As scientific meetings have proliferated, so they have degenerated into processions of poorly-constructed papers half-presented in inadequate time, thus generating little informed debate. Research results are not effectively communicated through such meetings. A well-constructed meeting can be a powerful engine of dissemination and debate, but the contributions need to be selected with discrimination and papers allowed time for a full exposition so that constructive discussion and interaction is promoted. The proceedings of such meetings may then provide a working reference document for practical use. A number of meetings of this kind have previously been organised by the Institution of Civil Engineers (e.g. Hydraulic Modelling in Maritime Engineering, 1981) and this formula should be encouraged as a matter of policy.

| 6.5. | Accessibility |

In the present-day commercial world, the practising engineer no longer has the time to read and consider technical papers. Although an abstracting journal or a computer data base may provide a route to find relevant published research results, this does not in itself make the results accessible in a practical sense. The practitioner works primarily to a preferred set of text-books or manuals, probably dating from his under-graduate or postgraduate studies. There is a clear need for a professionally recognised series of technical manuals that clearly present up-to-date information in an easily accessible and usable form. In some technical areas, this is provided by CIRIA publications and trade Research Associations. Good examples can be seen in the US Bureau of Reclamation series of Technical Monographs and Design Manuals, and in the Manuals and Reports on Engineering Practice compiled by the American Society of Civil Engineers (ASCE). The ASCE defines a manual as

> '. . . an orderly presentation of facts on a particular subject, supplemented by an analysis of limitations and applications of these facts. It contains information useful to the average engineer in his everyday work, rather than findings that may be useful only occasionally or rarely. It is not in any sense a 'standard,' however; nor is it elementary or so conclusive as to provide a 'rule of thumb' for non-engineers. Furthermore, material in this series, in distinction from a paper (which expresses only one person's observations or opinions), is the work of a committee or group selected to assemble and express information on a specific topic . . . . When published each work shows the names of the committee by which it was compiled and indicates clearly the several process through which it has passed in review, in order that its merit may be definitely understood.'

It is precisely this form of access to research results that the engineer needs: comprehensive, interpretative and authoritative. However, such manuals cannot be produced on a shoe-string solely by collating voluntary contributions: this requires funding at a level commensurate with the importance of the task. It is the role of the Institution of Civil Engineers, as the 'learned society' of the profession, to open a dialogue with the research funders and the civil engineering users to determine how such a series of manuals can be organised and funded. There is undoubtedly scope for co-operation and collaboration with the ASCE in this, and this avenue should be fully explored.

6.6.   Structure and status

It is extremely important that the status of any kind of publication should be well defined, as in the case of the ASCE manuals. There are many different levels to which research results can be distilled so as to become accessible, and the user needs to know unequivocally what reliance he can place upon the document to which he refers. From the user's point of view there are four requirements, as listed below:

(a)   an awareness of what information exists, and where to find it

(b)   a 'translation' of that information into simple terms that are easily understood, with an indication of its significance and application

(c)   a reassurance that the information is well-founded, that it has been proved in practice and its limitations are clearly defined

(d)   guidance on how to use the information in actual practice, through simple design aids, manuals, examples etc.

The issue is complicated by the sheer diversity of the civil engineering industry which means that there are many organisations working in parallel, but whose fields of interest do overlap, thereby causing confusion. Some of these organisations — institutions, associations, federations, societies — who publish their own reports, attempt to structure them so as to give some indication of differences in status. However, inevitably, each does it in its own way to different standards, and it is rare to have systematic procedures to assess and upgrade information, as distinct from simple revision.

One organisation which clearly grades its reports is the Fédération Internationale de la Précontrainte (FIP), and it is interesting to look at its system. In descending order, the FIP has:

Recommendations
Guides to Good Practice
Technical Reports
State-of-the-art Reports

Technical work in the FIP is in the hands of its Commissions, which are made up of people possessing detailed knowledge of the subject and who, between them, represent a fair cross-section of the industry (research, design, construction, building control, etc.). Any Commission, at the reporting stage, has to decide (within broad FIP guidelines) on the status of the information it is about to produce. Moreover, the work of the Commissions is continuous, and there is an incentive to review the position at intervals and to produce a higher grade report, if appropriate. Examples of how documents, other than journals and meetings proceedings, produced by other bodies in the UK might fit into this system are shown in Table 1 (which is far from exhaustive).

Table 1 clearly suggests that there is a possible solution to the structured dissemination of research. If the different status levels could be agreed, and defined within fairly close limits, then all organisations concerned with the dissemination of research information could be encouraged to work within this common framework. This is an approach that should be actively and energetically pursued, because the present

Table 1. Examples of types of publication produced by various organisations

	BSI	BRE	CIRIA	C&CA	Concrete Society	ICE
Recommendations	Codes, Standards					Standards and Specifications
Guides to good practice	Drafts for development	Digests	Guides Manuals	Development reports Advisory notes	Current practice sheets	Guides
Technical reports		Reports	Research reports	Technical reports	Technical reports	Technical reports
State-of-the-art Reports			Technical notes			ICE conference proceedings

system of having Codes and Standards as, effectively, the only accepted means of communicating information of any standing within the industry is unhealthy in terms of both R&D and technology transfer.

6.7 The way forward

Engineering research is of little practical value if it is not translated into engineering knowledge and practice. There is a common but fallacious premise that researchers can somehow be pressured or cajoled into applying more of their research budgets to improving their level of communication with the industry. The researchers themselves generally have neither the training nor the aptitude for this important task, and academic institutions could assist by placing more emphasis on this aspect of the researcher's skill. Nevertheless, the interpretation of research results and their dissemination in an accessible and usable form to the engineering profession is a skill in itself. This needs to be recognised through a willingness both to fund and to organise that as a separate function.

The advent of more sophisticated retrieval systems from wider data bases using computer technology is making the interrogation of the bank of literature references easier and more thorough. The initiative of the Science and Engineering Research Council in circulating a 'Civil Engineering Newsletter' containing up-to-date information on current research projects is also welcomed as a means of making the engineering profession aware of research in progress. This would be reinforced by inclusion of a 'Research Focus' in 'New Civil Engineer' as a regular feature. However, while all these developments serve to heighten an awareness of past and present research, they do not in themselves disseminate the results. The practising engineer basically needs a structured series of authoritative documents that interpret and present relevant research in a form that is both accessible and usable. It is important that the status of such documents is both clearly defined and scrupulously protected.

The Institution of Civil Engineers, as the 'learned society' of the profession, should take the initiative by entering into an active dialogue with research funders to determine how positive dissemination of research results can be financed as an activity in its own right, and by acting as sponsor and catalyst for the production of research reviews across its whole field of interest. It should seek, in dialogue with the wider engineering profession, to create a structured framework of reports which have a clearly defined status that is understood and recognised by the practising engineer. In this context, the Institution should also undertake a thorough review of the range of publications that it has inherited over the past 100 years, and reshape it to meet the needs of the present and the future.

The funding of the proposals for dissemination should be budgeted as part of construction research expenditure.

7. APPLICATION OF RESULTS FROM RESEARCH

7.1. Preface

Good application of results from research requires stronger two-way links between research and practice. Improved integration between these facets is essential for the effective operation of the civil engineering industry as a whole. This requires co-ordinated effort and a determination to commit results to assessment in real situations in order to demonstrate that innovations are practicable, effective and durable in the circumstances of prevailing workmanship, specification, standards, variations of materials and resulting use.

If the problems discussed in earlier chapters of structuring information into usable forms and of disseminating it can be solved, the industry will have achieved part of what is necessary to bring the fruits of research into practice. Nevertheless, there remain the areas of education and training, motivation and communication so as to ensure proper use of research investment.

Effective application depends very much on the nature, scale and scope of the problem being researched. At its simplest, research may be needed for straight problem solving in a one-off application. Here, all of the parties involved are aware, and there is good communication and understanding — and hence few difficulties are involved in application. This is true even if the single application is substantial or highly innovative — requiring the focusing of all available skills, tools and resources on the successful completion of the project. This is problem solving in the grand manner, and works well because it is still a singular situation.

Most of the difficulties in applying research arise when the research is done by the R&D community at large and has to be used by practice at large without the benefit of direct communication.

7.2. Education and training

The provision of structured information, if carried out properly, provides the basic means of communication — for education and training — at a professional level. Such a system would be of benefit to education and training establishments and to all those concerned with continuing professional development. The failure to apply existing knowledge was identified as a major problem in the NEDO Report, which also called for the development of a common basis of understanding of the construction process. It is suggested that this structured system would provide that understanding — at a professional level at least. Still at the professional level, design and construction are often quite separate procedures. In the training of staff, there is a need to make them consider, in a more conscious way, how the structure they conceive of will actually be put together — buildability. There is a further need — beginning at undergraduate level — to get a better balance between the numerate processes associated with strength evaluation and the less quantifiable (but equally important) aspects of design associated with performance in service (movement, serviceability, durability, etc.).

There remains the additional need for training of site personnel. No matter how technology may change or improve, there will always be a need for skilled operatives and supervisors who know not only what they are doing but also why it is important to do it well.

An analysis of defects in in-service performance reveals that, irrespective of the material used, nearly 90% of faults are due to deficiencies in design or construction — split more or less equally. This clearly emphasises the need for more education and training, as mentioned above, as well as supporting the NEDO Report call for a proper understanding of the construction process among all members of the industry. Client bodies selecting firms on the basis of cheapest price restrict the industry's capacity to spend more on education and training.

7.3. Communication

In considering the effective application of research in practice, and in deriving more efficient methods of ensuring that that which is known is actually applied, it should be emphasised that practice itself is constantly changing. Unless this is recognised, and these changes are monitored, full benefit from R&D will not be obtained. Practice is therefore a moving target and technology tranfer has to be a two-way process. An essential element of this is feedback, covering the design and construction processes on the one hand, and the in-service performance of structures on the other.

Change can come in many forms, and for widely differing reasons. It is often slow, almost undetectable in the short-term, as in the case of material properties or in producing more slender structures. The introduction of an innovative construction technique usually has a higher profile, and changes due to altered performance requirements or more intense loadings can be quite dramatic: de-icing salts on bridges; energy savings in buildings; mechanical handling in industrial structures; building on bad or made-up ground, etc.

Slow change is not monitored effectively, although this can be significant over a period. Major changes frequently just 'happen', often without a full appreciation of possible secondary or 'knock-on' effects. In both cases, effective feedback is an essential element in integrating R&D more closely with practice. It could, and should, be undertaken by the research community, with the added benefit of bringing researchers and practitioners closer together.

There is growing interest in developing QA procedures, not only for materials and components but also for design and construction as a whole. In part, this is a positive response from a section of the industry in an effort to reduce defects, which feedback from in-service performance has identified. Specifications and Codes of Practice, associated with materials, design and construction, are generally expressed in terms of *performance* requirements or prescriptions. These are important, but the fact that QA procedures are concerned with *methods* — how to achieve a required performance or to meet a prescription and to check that this has been done — will enhance basic understanding at all levels, since it implies proper organisation and a significant contribution by people.

7.4. Motivation

The ideal situation in R&D and technology transfer terms is when men and money are properly matched to motivation (the three 'Ms'). This match is not made at present — a fact identified in the NEDO Report.

There are a variety of reasons for the reluctance to apply research, which range from concern over legal liability to the need for short-term economies in the face of price competition. However, if the money that can be made available is used to bring selected areas of research through a thorough development process, the industry will be better able to introduce innovations. However, clients should review the increasing practice of choosing the cheapest price, not only for construction but also for design; a 'Value for Money' approach which gives equal weight to the quality of the proposals and the personnel would lead to improvements in the product and more innovation. The recent shift to selecting consultants on the basis of cheapest price is likely to reduce both their financial capability to spend time on innovations and their motivation to do so.

8.   ORGANISING RESEARCH AND DEVELOPMENT

8.1.   The current situation   The major bodies which provide support for construction research and development are listed in Chapter 9 under Funding, and they show that substantial proportions of this R&D are funded by both the private and public sectors. The Government Departments of Transport and the Environment and the Science and Engineering Research Council (SERC) provide much of the public sector funding. These organisations, controlling the sources of funds, have determined systems of consultation with practitioners and other bodies that are appropriate to the purpose for which they fund and/or carry out research. Systems in operation for Government departments and some of the research contractors involved with civil engineering research are as follows:

1.   *DoE*

(a)   *Construction Industry Directorate (Sponsorship Funding).* Advice on this programme has been provided by the Research Strategy Committee through NEDO's EDCs for building and civil engineering. The Institution is represented on the EDCs; the RSC included four individuals, together with the Chairman, who are members of the Institution. The future consultative mechanism will depend on action following the NEDO Report.

(b)   *PSA, Water Directorate etc.* These operate programmes to serve their public purchasing and policy development needs; and they use internal committees drawing on advice from industry as and when required.

(c)   *BRE.* Practitioner advice on the BRE programme has been obtained from the RSC and the Building Regulation Advisory Committee (BRAC), who advise by way of the DoE, and through a system of appointed 'visitors', some of whom are individual members of the Institution. Informal advice is also obtained through working and collaborating with industry.

2.   *DTp*

(a)   Research needs, commissioned to assist with public purchasing responsibilities for the transport infrastructure, are established by professional divisions who, in turn seek advice from relevant outside organisations.

(b)   *TRRL.* This also operates a system of 'visitors' and has advisory working groups in some areas.

3.   *SERC*

The Committee structure of the SERC is well defined, and the Institution has members on the Council, the Engineering Board, and the Environment Committee and its Sub-Committees. The Environment Committee covers responsibility for transport engineering, building, marine technology and civil engineering. The Civil Engineering Sub-Committee, with the assistance of four subject co-ordinators, has responsibility for controlling and developing an enlarged civil engineering programme. The co-ordinators are assisted by steering groups and, in addition, a DoE official has been appointed with responsibility for co-ordinating civil engineering research funded by the DoE and the

SERC, and to encourage collaboration with Government departments and industry.

4. *WRc*

The WRc is funded almost entirely by the Regional Water Authorities. Its Council and committee, advising on and controlling the research programme, consist mainly of RWA staff, representing each Authority's interest.

5. *CIRIA*

As a company limited by guarantee, CIRIA is controlled by a council (Board of Directors) elected by the members (shareholders), and is supported by a system of 'expert' committees which identify research requirements, participate in individual projects and advise on the dissemination of results. Some 400 practitioners, mostly members of the Institution, are involved in CIRIA's council, and its principal committees contain a majority of Institution members.

In addition, there are other Government departments (e.g. MAFF, DHSS), research associations and laboratories with civil engineering research interests. The Government departments commission research to assist with their policy responsibilities while the research associations and laboratories serve their client needs. Much of the research provides a general public benefit even though their individual programmes are developed to meet client needs. There is little formal co-ordination between the organisations but informal links at research level probably prevent wasteful duplication.

8.2. Co-ordination

The Institution has welcomed the efforts being made by the DoE to gain some co-ordination of research interest, and it recognises that those bodies with subjects which have common links are beginning to achieve worthwhile collaboration. Voluntary collaboration, which by definition provides advantages for all the parties involved, has the best potential for securing increased co-ordination. There are, however, limitations to current co-ordinating activities and these are as follows:

(i) The allocation of research resources tends to respond to pressure groups as well as to the shorter term needs of those prepared to pay, and there is the possibility that important gaps are not covered.

(ii) The lack of involvement in research by industrial partners limits the practitioner's ability to provide views on needs for research.

(iii) There is an ability to maintain areas of research but limited resources for keeping the balance of the programme under review. It is felt that important gaps between programmes of different organisations can occur especially during periods of restraint. Research underpinning the needs of local authorities is a current example.

(iv) Although some proposals for far-sighted basic research do gain support, the lack of active encouragement for such research with an allocated resource is considered to be stifling good proposals from coming forward.

(v) There is an inability to bring together portfolios of research and to assess the worth of strategic research within the context of applied and basic programmes.

(vi) There are limited resources available for establishing and monitoring well-planned collaborative research. Collaborative research can provide profitable links with the research of Government departments, other research organisations and industry. Actions to encourage and to manage collaboration needs personnel.

(vii) There is limited activity in ensuring timely dissemination and use of research results. Planning for and financial provision for dissemination is not generally made during the development of proposals for research.

The discussion on Selection and Implementation of Research Projects in Chapter 4 amply demonstrates the need for strategic selection of research, the comprehensive process required to ensure its effective use, and the necessity of carefully examining the balance of research needed in any particular problem. These vital aspects require the overview and co-ordination that can only be provided by a central body composed of industry, researchers and sponsors' representatives.

The problems of Dissemination of Research Results discussed in Chapter 6 are the most significant facing the industry, and they require urgent solution. On account of the number of organisations involved in this process and the present lack of defined standards, a co-ordinating body is essential to lead the industry forward to effective use of even existing information.

The Task Force Report (1981) and, more recently, the NEDO Report on 'Strategy for Construction R&D' both identified a need for more national cohesion and co-ordination of research and dissemination. This need stems from the view that the system for construction R&D in the UK has evolved into a rather introspective approach. The public funding (with the exception of the DoE's Sponsorship programme and that funded by the SERC) provides for the individual policy needs of Government departments and is not necessarily geared to achieving, as a spin-off, maximum advantage for UK industry or local government.

It is feared that the tight schedules being imposed on Government research establishments and the research associations is tending to squeeze out strategic research to address the more immediate problems. Some degree of national co-ordination is needed to ensure a proper balanced portfolio of research which addresses longer term needs as well as those of the immediate future. Development of the national policy should also examine the advantages and scope for relaxing the constraining manpower and annual budgeting policies imposed on the management of BRE and TRRL. A significant increase in industry involvement with the work of these laboratories can be achieved only with a more flexible approach to manpower and financial budgeting.

It was with the above in mind that the Task Force recommended that the DoE and the DTp establish a Board with responsibility for research, and that the organisations with interest in research (including the Institution) should ensure adequate cross-membership of their respective committees. The RSC also recommended the establishment of a Construction Research Board for construction R&D, increased industry participation and interest in R&D, the raising of additional funds for R&D, periodic generation of R&D priorities, the maintenance of national R&D capabilities and substantial improvements in technology transfer.

**8.3.   Value of industry
         involvement**

Industrial involvement in R&D is vital. Industry's commitment to support for R&D will assist with the allocation of priorities and will provide direct avenues for achieving application of research results. Participation in a national programme through a collaborative or club-type approach, such as instituted by the DTI for the manufacturing industry, could provide an affordable route for firms to maintain access to expertise in areas of interest.

It is in the nature of things that industries will normally be prepared to contribute to — and indeed carry out — research leading to some immediately recognisable benefit. Much of the private sector R&D is aimed at product development. Most of it is well done, but this type of research cannot resolve the many broadly based issues for which industry as a whole requires a sound knowledge base.

Contractors' immediate interests are in construction management, manufacturers' in product research and consultants' in design aids and drawing production. Unfortunately, the major problems do not fall neatly within these categories and have to be defined, co-ordinated and solved on an industry-wide basis, but with the active involvement of all these interests.

**8.4.   Relationship with
         SERC**

The co-ordination of R&D should be in close liaison with the SERC as well as with the many other interested organisations. The civil engineering activities of the SERC should be strongly linked with the user industry. This could be achieved through the SERC mechanism of allocating directorate status to all its civil engineering and building activities, including those covered by its Transport Sub-Committee. The status of a directorate along with the delegated powers placed on it by the SERC would better facilitate the fostering of industrial support. A balance of research and cross-fertilisation of disciplines would be made possible by bringing all civil engineering and building together within one Directorate.

8.5.   EEC research

A co-ordinating body would be well placed to influence, where desirable, EEC funding initiatives on research programmes appropriate to the UK. It could also ensure dissemination of information on EEC funding projects. It is important to note, however, that the UK's contribution to EEC research is likely to be at the expense of the UK Government funded research; hence the need to ensure UK interests are best served through collaborative funding by the EEC.

8.6.   R&D facilities

There is considerable scope for more shared use of facilities which, in turn, could bring the added advantage of increasing the scope for collaborative working by different research organisations with industry. The mechanism needed to increase shared usage is not necessarily expensive, nor should it be heavy-handed, but encouragement and changed policies, as implied in Section 8.2, are needed. A co-ordinating body, such as the Construction Research Board, proposed by the Research Strategy Committee would be well placed to develop appropriate policy. The recent example of a jointly funded facility (SERC and Hydraulics Research Limited with backing from MAFF), currently being commissioned for use by a group of universities in collaboration with HRL, is welcomed. There is a need, however, to ensure that the UK moves towards the right balance of facilities covering all building and civil engineering subjects.

8.7. **Support for a co-ordinating body**

The Institution supported the EDC's major recommendation that a Construction Research Board (CRB) should be established. In supporting the recommendation for such a co-ordinating body, the following is stressed:

(a) The co-ordinating body should be an umbrella organisation to all existing research groups; as an 'enabling' organisation, it will require adequate funding.

(b) The performance of the co-ordinating body will be highly dependent on the calibre and motivation of the Chairman and members, who should be appointed as individuals, not as representatives of any particular sector, but nevertheless be broadly based so as to be able to reflect the views of the construction industry on R&D. The Chairman should be a respected name in industry. The co-ordinating body should also include senior civil servants, able to report directly to their respective Secretaries of State.

(c) Notwithstanding the need for a broadly based body, the co-ordinating body should be small enough in number to be effective.

(d) The co-ordinating body must be provided with an adequate staff who are highly competent, both technically and administratively. Either a new secretariat should be formed or this function could be devolved to CIRIA.

8.8. **Action needed**

The current situation — its strengths and limitations — and the Institution's views in relation to recommendations made by major committees assessing organisational needs for research in civil engineering and/or building, have been covered in the previous sections. In summary, a list of the most essential actions for achieving better value from building and civil engineering research are given below.

(i) A co-ordinating body, with executive functions to enable it to attract change, should be established. It needs resource for pump priming to encourage industry participation, for monitoring research and for commissioning special studies to identify needs. Its potential for success would be enhanced by setting targets by which to measure its achievement. (8.7)

(ii) Collaborative programmes, which have well-balanced research portfolios containing long and short-term goals, need to be initiated within the UK. (8.2)

(iii) There has to be an improved flexibility for manpower and financial management of BRE and TRRL. (8.2)

(iv) An SERC directorate for all SERC's civil engineering and building activities, including those covered by its transport sub-committee, should be established. (8.4)

(v) International collaborative programmes — particularly within the EEC — for subjects where the added costs of collaboration are outweighed by the economies and synergy resulting from such a joint action, need to be initiated (8.5)

(vi) Joint industry/Government funded research should be

encouraged, and the collaborative club principle developed. (8.3)

(vii) The SERC should be encouraged to make special provision for and promotion by the SERC of funding for best proposals for far-sighted basic research. (8.2)

(viii) Planning should be undertaken and financial provision made for the dissemination of research. (8.2).

9. FUNDING

9.1. Introduction

The Task Force Report considered availability of funds for research and noted that the level of funds was low compared with other nations and that it needed to be increased. The position is much the same today. The NEDO Report 'Strategy for Construction R&D' gives an estimate of construction R&D expenditure in 1984 as £146.5 million, representing 0.65% of UK construction output. Of this figure, some £80 million comes from manufacturers and £58.5 million from the public sector. Only £8 million is credited to contractors and consultants. There can be little doubt that the total level should be increased if the UK is to continue to compete internationally. The manufacturers are market motivated and see R&D as an essential part of the process of product development and marketing. Consultants, contractors and building owners often cannot see a direct benefit to themselves from R&D. Most construction work is not patentable, is 'one-off' in nature and is specific to a particular location. Also, it cannot be marketed as a product, and is subject to competitive tendering, with local companies frequently having an advantage. Progress in construction R&D leads to improvement in 'techniques', as distinct from 'products' as in the case of manufacturing. As improvements in techniques cannot be patented, and such improvements are freely available to all competitors, there is no repayment for such investment. It is solely the client and general public who benefit.

The figures quoted in the above paragraph are for 'commissioned' research; they take no account of the important activity of disseminating information which is going on continuously within the work of the Institution and BSI and elsewhere. An estimate of the direct costs of this dissemination of research at the Institution is conservatively put at £500 000 per annum and this could be multiplied several times if other institutions and relevant conferences were included. If a wider definition of research is taken, virtually the whole turnover of the Institution could be taken coupled with the value of time of all members working on committees and attending meetings. This would amount to several millions of pounds. The Concise Oxford Dictionary's definition, 'the endeavour to discover new or to collate old facts by scientific study of a subject', would certainly embrace much of the Institution's work. It would also include the substantial efforts by practitioners in connection with specific projects, and so result in a significant increase in R&D credited to the private sector.

The public sector is the client for approximately 50% of all construction in the UK, including at least 80% of the civil engineering element. The community is, therefore, the main beneficiary of R&D. The benefits include quality, safety, economy and efficiency of the product and of the national infrastructure as a whole and, in addition, a substantial net contribution to the nation's activities overseas. It seems inescapable that the major part of construction R&D should be paid for from public funds. This is not to say that the Institution does not advocate industrial participation. Indeed, it is seen as essential. The Institution also wishes to encourage an increase in university based research with industrial participation. The SERC already has a number of such schemes funded and it is to be hoped that the number of these can be increased.

Current sources of funds for R&D are diverse and these are summarised in Section 9.10.

9.2. Structure of the industry

The structure of the construction industry is also relevant to the problem of raising additional R&D funds in the private sector. The number of large contractors with, say, over 1000 employees is small and is decreasing, and there is a great number of small firms. It is only the larger firms who could make funds available for R&D, other than by the application of some form of compulsory levy; any voluntary increase in R&D funds would be borne by the largest firms, thereby making them less competitive and again tending to increase the use of sub-contracting. Similarly, it may be argued that voluntary R&D funding would be disproportionately borne by the larger consultants, thus reducing their ability to compete in the present demanding market.

Contractors rarely own their product; they are usually paid on a monthly basis for their work. Hence it could be inappropriate to express the value of R&D work as a percentage of turnover. The low capital involvement is not a structure likely to encourage major R&D investment and, therefore, ways have to be found to persuade the real investors in construction, namely the clients, to spend a similar proportion to that of other industries on R&D. As improvements in efficiency and durability are directly of benefit to the clients and not to the industry, it is essential that the client should pay. However, there have been negative responses to sample approaches made to private developers, and without the force of law this is unlikely to be a fruitful source of additional funds.

9.3. Effects of competition

One of the causes of the reluctance of the construction industry to invest in R&D is the highly competitive nature of the market. Construction companies have savagely to cut all costs not immediately necessary in order to secure work in competitive tendering, and this is aggravated by the excessively long tender lists required by both public and private sector clients. To the Board of Directors of a construction company, most R&D is of doubtful value in giving the company a tendering edge on any immediate project. It is definitely not of immediate value and it is therefore likely to be axed. A change in the tendering system could ease this position and bring other benefits such as improved quality control and fewer claims. With the present depressed level of construction activity, it would need a positive move by the public sector to secure any change in this direction. Hence the hope of achieving voluntary increases in R&D funding from contractors is fading. Much the same may now be said for consultants who are facing increased fee competition both at home and abroad.

9.4. Differing categories of R&D work

Work which is intended to be widely disseminated through the construction industry and which is aimed at, for example, better practice, improved safety or better quality products has such a wide range of beneficiaries that collection of funding from all of them is impractical. A high proportion of funding from Government, as a proxy customer, is therefore appropriate. It is unreasonable to expect large contributions from individual companies who receive little, if any, competitive advantage from the work.

Work which is of primary benefit to Government as a customer for public works should be funded primarily by Government.

Work which gives commercial advantage to individual companies should be funded primarily by the companies that benefit. However, by analogy with the Support for Innovation programme of the DTI, an element of Government subsidy would be appropriate — even for single companies — when there are significant externalities, when the technical risks are long term and the beneficiaries uncertain, or when the financial risks are large compared with the size of the company. In particular, substantial Government support, say at the 50% level, is appropriate for pre-competitive collaborative programmes. There is little DTI funding for construction or DoE funding direct to contractors or consultants. The DoE should consider adoptive schemes for supporting industry based R&D along similar lines to those adopted by the DTI.

9.5. Use of levies to increase funding

The various levies suggested in the NEDO Report 'Strategy for Construction R&D' would require legislation to make them effective and could be administratively complex, resulting in another layer of expensive bureaucracy. Perhaps the simplest might be a levy on building controls but there would have to be none of the (public sector) exceptions to such controls. It is essential that any form of levy be uniformly spread to avoid an uneven load to one sector, thus making it less competitive. There is also the danger that labour only sub-contracting would escape a particular levy and hence its growth could be further encouraged.

Any suggestion that a public sector tender list be restricted to companies having a 'satisfactory' level of R&D would be unfair, as this would result in an uneven spread of the R&D load within the industry.

It is believed that there is an inherent dislike of levies within the industry who would see levies as a tax not under their control, and which could develop a bureaucracy of their own, thereby reducing the efficiency in the use of the funds. One possible way to overcome this would be to use the existing machinery of the Construction Industry Training Board. The CITB has the authority under the 1982 Industrial Training Act to raise a per capita levy on contractors, and in 1985 levied £45 million in this way. By Act of Parliament, this levy could be increased and the increase passed to the Construction Research Board proposed by the NEDO Report. If the research element of this levy is on an identical basis to the training levy, the increase in administrative costs should be small. This idea is, of course, open to the objection that no additional funds would be raised from consultants or local authorities. There may also be the risk of encouraging the growth of lump labour. It must be recorded that the Institution has not discussed this idea with the CITB but it is put forward as one way, even if flawed, of raising R&D funds by levy. There would seem to be no totally satisfactory solution to raising money by levy.

There would seem to be little alternative to the substantial increase in funds provided by the Government for general purpose research within the construction industry. Funds may be generated by the private sector, as stated above, for research which is more specific in nature, and this could be promoted by use of public sector subsidies.

9.6. Importance of industrial involvement

Notwithstanding the above call for increased public sector R&D funds, the Institution recognises the importance of industrial involvement in R&D. In particular, industry must help with the assessment of R&D requirements and the allocation of priorities. An involvement during the course of development work is highly desirable to ensure that the course of the work continues to be directed to the most useful objectives. To achieve this, it is desirable that there should be industrial financial participation in the R&D; while this does not need to be a high percentage, it must not be negligible. To target at 50% or more contribution by industry is unrealistic.

Obtaining R&D funds from building owners, particularly in the private sector, is likely to prove difficult and the effort spent unrewarded. Most clients commission buildings infrequently, while those that do have a major programme are likely to be interested in development only for their own specialised requirements.

| 9.7. | **Collaborative clubs** | The collaborative club approach, in which a group of companies subscribe to an R&D project, can be useful and should be encouraged. Certain universities and private research companies have successfully adopted this idea. To a certain extent it is true to say that once a company has joined such a club, it is reluctant to leave in case a competitor, who is also a member, may gain some advantage. |

| 9.8. | **EEC funding** | Maximum use should be made of the funding opportunities available within the EEC. The procedures for obtaining such funds are complicated and not well known. A small group skilled in progressing EEC funding applications is needed to assist appropriate organisations seeking research funds from this source. |

| 9.9. | **Conclusions on funding** | In view of the structure of the construction industry and the present highly competitive situation, the present efforts of industry and the Institutions in R&D are creditable. An increase in effort must be led by the Government, and the lead must be clear if industry is to be encouraged to follow with its own increase in contribution. This should not be difficult for the Government to accept, as it is unquestionably the largest client for the construction industry. With direct funding, the Government will have greater direction of a co-ordinated R&D effort which must benefit the nation as a whole. |

Emphasising the above call for increased Government involvement in construction R&D is the small amount of funds presently available for basic research and the low level of public sector R&D funds available for construction, compared with some of our overseas competitors and also compared with the levels of funds in other industries such as agriculture. In this connection, the Institution notes with concern the Report to the Secretary of State for Education and Science from the Advisory Board for the Research Councils dated April 1986 and authorised for publication in July 1986. That Board views 'with dismay' the 'steady decline' in the real value of public funding for science and engineering research through the research councils. The Report goes on to record as stating:

'We cannot assume that the growing gap between the capability of the science base and national needs will be closed even partly by private funds. Our recently completed study of the scope for extending private funding of research found that, for sound commercial reasons, industry is not prepared to commit its funds to the speculative, pre-competitive research which the science base exists to support. Although there is scope for an expansion of collaborative research with industry in strategic areas where applications are in sight, our study found that increased publicly-funded investment is the essential pre-condition for engaging more private sector funds through collaborative programmes.'

Their views agree with the opinions of this Institution which have been independently formed and noted in this chapter.

These remarks relate to direct funding of research and development work. It is even more difficult to see how increased funds may be available from the private sector for the dissemination of the results of research, short of an imposed levy which is not favoured. However, dissemination is as important as research itself and without it research could be wasted.

9.10 Existing sources of funding

Public sector

DoE: *CID:* to Building Research Establishment, Hydraulics Research Ltd, Construction Industry Research & Information Association, Building Services Research & Information Association and Timber Research and Development Association for projects in support of industry and required by the DoE.

PSA: for work required by PSA — to Building Research Establishment, Construction Industry Research & Information Association, and many others.

Water Directorates: for work required by the Directorate.

Housing and Construction Directorate: for work required by the Directorate.

The majority of the work required within the DoE is directed to the Building Research Establishment to be undertaken either in-house or by placing external contracts.

DTp: work required by the Department is directed to the Transport and Road Research Laboratory to be undertaken either in-house or by placing external contracts.

DEn: primarily for work required by the Department on offshore structures, atomic energy and alternative forms of energy and for conservation of energy (e.g. in housing). The Offshore Supplies Office places contracts in sponsorship of British offshore industry.

MAFF: work required by the Ministry, particularly for coastal protection and flood control.

DHSS: work required by the Department, i.e. hospital and health buildings.

ODA: work required by the ODA in support of its policies; primarily at the Building Research Establishment, Transport and Road Research Laboratory, Hydraulics Research Ltd, Institute of Geological Sciences.

MOD: work required by the Ministry, usually by way of PSA.

DTI: sponsorship of manufacturing industry — limited amount of construction, e.g. robotics, expert systems.

SERC: funded by the DES for research which is limited to universities and polytechnics and SERC wholly owned institutes.

NERC: geology, oceanography and marine biology, hydrology and so on, mostly at the British Geotechnical Society, Institute of Oceanographic Sciences, Institute of Marine Environmentalists, I. Terrestrial Ecology, etc.

Local Authorities: ad-hoc and very limited funding.

Regional Water Authorities: mostly for the Water Research Centre and in-house research, but some funding available for specific projects required by individual Regional Water Authorities.

British Rail: mostly for its own laboratories (Derby).

British Steel Corporation: mostly by way of Constrado.

British Airports Authority

CEGB: own laboratories at Leatherhead and Gloucester.

British Gas: own laboratories at Capenhurst.

UGC.

Private sector: Manufacturers

Brick — mostly in-house or by way of the British Ceramics Research Association.

Cement — in-house or by way of the Cement & Concrete Association.

Timber — by way of the Timber Research and Development Association.

Paint — mostly in-house or by way of the Paint Research Association.

Rubber & Plastics — mostly in-house or by way of the Rubber & Plastics Research Association.

Building Services — mostly in-house or by way of the Building Services Research Information Association.

Steel — mostly in-house or by way of Constrado.

Private sector: Contractors and consultants

Some in-house or by way of CIRIA and others; also significant contribution through participation in British Standards Institution committees. Institution of Civil Engineers activities and other bodies.

Others

EEC: funds available from various programmes, e.g. BRITE, EUREKA, etc.; UK could attract much more funding from EEC with a concerted effort; a centre of expertise in guiding applicants through the labyrinth of procedures to secure EEC funds is needed.

Insurers: generally unwilling to support construction research.

Property Developers: generally unwilling to support construction research.

BTG (formerly NRDC):   funds available for patentable development.

World Bank: for specific work related to Third World development.

Wolfson Foundation: rarely for construction projects.

10. THE ROLE OF THE INSTITUTION

10.1.   Introduction

This report has shown that the needs of research identified in the Task Force Report remain largely unresolved.

The major problems are:

– lack of overall co-ordination
– lack of strategic selection of R&D
– inadequate funding
– insufficient involvement of practitioners in defining research needs
– lack of processing and structuring of existing knowledge
– poor dissemination of data
– insufficient knowledge and use of research from other countries
– a separation of interest between researchers and practitioners.

With increased competition overseas and a need for better performance from scarce capital investment in construction at home, the industry, like all other industries, will become even more dependent on effective R&D and its dissemination to and use by practitioners.

10.2.   Market sector needs

Our studies have been based on those market sectors in construction in which civil engineering plays an important, and often dominant, role. The Institution, through its Engineering Group Boards and associated societies, could, if provided with the resources, help in the identification and promotion of the required research in these market sectors. The Group Boards and their societies embody designers, contractors, researchers and related professions and are, therefore, very suited to assisting in the defining of research needs. This suggestion was put forward in the response to the NEDO Report, and indeed the recent Coastal Engineering Research Panel Report is an example of what can be done by joining researchers and practitioners to define research needs.

Such efforts should be harmonised with CIRIA in order to avoid duplication.

In the case of building, which is a multi-disciplinary process, the Institution should invite the other engineering institutions involved in building (IStructE, CIBSE and IPHE), to join in defining the engineering research needs of that sector. If the RIBA wished to participate, the role could be extended to include architectural research.

However, the Institution's resources are limited and it already makes substantial contributions in time to learned society work. It is unlikely that the Institution could mount a continuing programme in all the areas without financial help.

10.3.   Publications

Chapter 6 on Dissemination of Research Results has identified the needs for:

– abstracting journals based on a sound framework of relevant key words

– structured information for practitioners based on nationally accepted definitions of information status

– research reviews.

The engineer today has more need of processed and structured information than for original papers, and the Institution should review its publications accordingly. The reporting of meritorious papers from overseas journals should be undertaken. A dialogue should be opened with funders to determine how a series of technical manuals with up-to-date information could be organised and funded.

The separation of practitioners and researchers into different interests is artificial and unproductive, and the Institution should consider publications based on market sectors spanning research, design and practice as a better means of integrating research and practice to the benefit of both researcher and practitioner.

The Institution should assist the promotion of a nationally accepted classification of status of published information.

10.4.	**Meetings**	Meetings need to be well constructed and selected with discrimination, with time for a full exposition so that constructive discussion and interaction are promoted. The proceedings of such meetings may then provide a reference document for practical use.

The Institution should continue to promote meetings as a matter of policy.

10.5.	**Bringing researchers and practitioners together**	The present separation of interests between practitioners and researchers is harmful to both. Research needs more guidance on the problems facing practitioners, and the opportunities for more test applications. In turn, practitioners need to be better informed of developments and to have their beliefs in the value of research strengthened through a better flow of useful information.

The publication of a 'Research Focus' on a regular basis and the dissemination of research news by 'New Civil Engineer' would help to ease this problem.

Every project has an R&D element within it, and besides the need for structured information, a readily accessible inventory of R&D in progress would be useful to practitioners. The Institution should co-operate with the proposed co-ordinating body in making this available.

Collaborative clubs are proposed in Section 9.7 as a means of promoting private industry's interest and financial involvement in research. The Institution should assist the formation of such clubs.

10.6.	**Funding and co-ordination**	As discussed in Chapter 9 on Funding, it is essential that those who finance and own the civil engineering product, from its inception through its construction and in use, are made to see the necessity of funding research and development, in addition to those who practice engineering.

The Institution should, in addition to its own considerable contribution, maintain pressure on Government to organise proper co-ordination and appropriate funding and be ready to respond if Government uses its power to remedy the overall framework.

10.7.	**ICE Research Sub-Committee**	Besides the work in this report, the ICE Research Sub-Committee has responded during the year to the NEDO Report, the House of Lords Select Committee on Civil Research and the organisation of the BRE. These activities indicate a need for a focus for research matters within the Institution.

If the Institution adopts the proposals in this report, there will also be a need to guide and co-ordinate the Engineering Group Boards' activities in research and to liaise with other committees on changes in publications and meetings policy.

There is also a need to follow up the present work with a biennial report on progress on the matters discussed in this report.

Each Group Board should form a Research Panel similar to, or in combination with, its Papers and Meetings Panel, with a brief to develop and promote research and its dissemination within each individual market sector.

The ICE Research Sub-Committee recommends that it should continue as a permanent Sub-Committee with a brief to co-ordinate the Institution's research interests and to help promote research and its dissemination as an integral part of civil engineering.

| 10.8. | **An Institution policy on research** |

It would be wasteful of resources, and it could even be counter-productive, for the Institution and its proposed Research Sub-Committee to undertake in isolation the various actions recommended in this Chapter. A clear policy should be developed defining the Institution's role in research and the limits within which it can work effectively. The function of the proposed co-ordinating body would have to be taken into account in developing the Institution's policy.

The Institution founded CIRIA 25 years ago because it recognised the need for an expansion in research directed towards the needs of practitioners, and it recognised also that a skilled research management staff was essential to the success of this work that, hitherto, had been the responsibility of the Institution's Research Committee. In both respects, the present is the same as the past. The important part of the Institution's policy should therefore be to continue to give strong support to CIRIA and also to encourage individual members to do so.

Members of the Institution also rely substantially on the research and information activities of the many research associations supported by manufacturers of materials and components, especially C&CA, Steel & Construction Industry, British Ceramics Ltd and TRADA. Similarly, members rely substantially on the supportive research and information activities of Government research establishments, especially BRE and TRRL, as well as the privatised HRL. The Institution of Geological Sciences, Institute of Hydrology and the Ordnance Survey are also important sources of information to the practitioner. The programmes of research supported by the SERC and NERC are also highly relevant.

All of these public and private funded organisations have their own management structures and methods of determining priorities for research. Nevertheless, they would all welcome well researched and well supported recommendations to include in their programmes. They would also welcome the Institution's support for realistic funding by their sponsors in both the private and public sectors.

The Institution's policy should therefore include the presentation of cases in support of specific R&D projects and programmes, including forward-looking research likely to lead to useful innovation.

The foregoing functions of making well-directed recommendations for R&D priorities by the Institution and high level pressure for adequate funding to the research organisations concerned, should form an important part of the Institution's policy.

Beyond this is the difficult but essential requirement of improving technology transfer. Although, through CIRIA, the various private sector and public sector organisations are already active in the field, the Institution is well placed to initiate the co-ordination of a national effort in co-operation with the major private and public sector research organisations.

The preparation of an Institution policy for R&D and technology transfer and its relationship to the proposed co-ordinating body would be an important task for the proposed Research Sub-Committee, for consideration by Council.

CONCLUSIONS AND RECOMMENDATIONS*

1.	**Progress since Task Force Report**	The principal recommendation of the 1981 Task Force Report that a co-ordinating body should be set up has not been put into effect. This remains a vital need for both civil engineering and building if research is to be selected, co-ordinated and managed to effective benefit. (2.3) Some progress has been made in improved funding and co-ordination with the SERC, but this alone is unequal to the magnitude and extent of the problems. (2.2)
2.	**The value of research and development**	An examination of benefits from earlier research and the cost of neglect in other areas demonstrate that the industry needs to be technically advanced. This is essential if the industry is to survive in overseas markets and is to provide durable, functional and cost efficient products at home. Research, development and dissemination are necessary functions to achieving technical advancement. (3.2 and 3.3)

3. Selection and implementation of research projects

(a) Commissioned research and development in construction are two aspects of a process which, to achieve successful application, requires the implementation of eight steps:

- discussions, involving industry, to determine need or priority
- options appraisal (review existing data, establish balance, set budget)
- research
- development
- structured information ⎫
- demonstration projects ⎬ *interactive*
- dissemination ⎭
- training

At present no one is responsible for ensuring that any piece of research is taken through all the steps. Consequently much good work remains blocked in the process and the investment is ineffective. (4.2)

Systems should be set up to programme, cost and review the eight stages in a research project and Researcher Managers appointed with the responsibility of bringing such projects to completion.

(b) In choosing options for funding, an appraisal of the disparity of knowledge between elements such as physical data, material standards, analysis and design methods, construction performance and operation is required so as to establish a balanced programme of

---

*Recommendations are shown in italics.

42

research. Very often research effort is distributed disproportionately between the elements. (4.3)

Careful consideration should be given to the proposals to ensure that the most important elements are researched. (4.3)

4.   **Development work**   (a)   The application of new or improved techniques or materials on a widespread scale without an exhaustive development programme puts scarce capital resources at risk and can bring such innovations into disrepute. (5.1 and 5.3)

Changes and innovations should not be implemented on a widespread scale until researchers and practitioners are satisfied with the degree of development. (5.1)

(b)   Demonstration projects are an essential part of the proving process in order to validate the innovation within the context of prevailing standards of design and workmanship etc. (5.2)

Clients with large rolling programmes of work must be encouraged to undertake demonstration projects as a routine. (5.2)

5.   **Dissemination**   (a)   Much engineering research is not readily usable by engineers and is not effectively applied or exploited. This is due to the present undeveloped nature of the available information, which needs to be collated, reworked and interpreted in terms of practical application. (6.1 and 6.3)

A change of attitude is required on the part of funders, examiners and publishers to allow such application orientated research to take place and to endow the research interpreters who would undertake it with intellectual respectability. (6.3)

The importance of reviewing, validating and structuring research knowledge from home and abroad should be recognised and acted upon. The engineering interpreters who carry out this function should be professionally recognised for the significant value of this type of work. (6.2 and 6.3)

Professional engineering journals, including the ICE Proceedings, should be pressed to accept research papers as meritorious. (6.3)

(b)   Publications and meetings tend to separate into those on research for researchers and those on practice for practitioners, and exchange between the two is poor. There is a proliferation of journals, meetings and conferences which is confusing to both. (6.4)

There is a need to promote the abstracting of journals to provide authoritative technical guidance. This should be grouped according to market sector based on a sound index of relevant key words. (6.4)

(c)   The practising engineer does not have the time to digest research papers, and there is a need for more structured information divided into levels which are readily understood as to their status. The present variety of categories used by different research bodies needs rationalising into a nationally accepted system. (6.5)

A nationally accepted classification of the status of published information should be a priority task of the co-ordinating body. (6.6)

(d) The practising engineer works primarily to a preferred set of text books or manuals, and there is a clear need for a professionally recognised series of technical manuals that presents up-to-date information in a usable form. (6.5 and 6.6)

The Institution should open a dialogue with the research funders and users to determine how such a series can be organised and funded. (6.7)

The interests of researchers and practitioners should be integrated as much as possible through meetings and publications. (6.4)

(e) The funding of these proposals should be budgeted as part of construction research expenditure. (6.7)

A substantial proportion of the overall research budget should be allocated to this activity. (6.3)

6. **Application of results from research**

(a) In addition to dissemination, the issues of education and training, motivation and feedback need to be resolved in order to promote the application of research. (7.1)

(b) Most faults are due to deficiencies in design or construction which emphasises the need for better education and training for both professional staff and skilled operatives. (7.2)

The construction industry needs to spend more on training, and clients should be encouraged to review firms' efforts on training staff as part of 'Value for Money' selection procedure. (7.2 and 7.3)

(c) Reasons for a reluctance to innovate range from legal liabilities to the need for short-term economies in the industry resulting from price competition. The recent shift to selecting consultants on the basis of cheapest price is likely to affect adversely both quality and innovation. (7.4)

Major clients should be encouraged to select firms with an innovative record as part of a 'Value for Money' selection procedure. (7.4)

(d) Technology transfer is a two-way process of which an essential element is feedback covering both design and construction processes and in-service performance. Such interchange of views can come about through the bringing together of researchers and practitioners through meetings, publications and collaborative clubs as advocated in other chapters. (7.3)

Bringing researchers and practitioners together should be promoted by both the Institution and the proposed co-ordinating body.

7. **Organising research and development**

(a) There is an overwhelming need for a central body as a co-ordinating and policy setting organisation for research, development and dissemination. The co-ordinating body should be broadly based so as to be able to reflect the views of the construction industry. (8.2)

The Government should set up this co-ordinating body and ensure that it has appropriate funds to carry out its work. (8.7)

(b) The co-ordination of R&D should be in close liaison with the SERC, and this liaison would be enhanced if the SERC's civil engineering activities, along with those covered by its building and transport sub-committees, were organised as a separate directorate. (8.4)

The SERC should be persuaded to set up a civil engineering and building directorate embracing its civil engineering, building and transport activities. (8.8)

(c) There is a need for collaborative programmes to have well balanced portfolios containing long-term and short-term goals. (8.3)

The SERC should be encouraged to make special provision to promote the funding of more far-sighted basic research in addition to subject directed programmes. (8.8)

(d) International collaborative programmes could be developed, particularly within the EEC, for subjects where the added costs of collaboration are outweighed by the economies and synergy from joint action. (8.8)

The proposed co-ordinating body should seek to influence the direction of EEC funding of research and provide professional guidance in processing appropriate UK research applications. (8.5)

(e) Joint industry/Government funded research could be of significant advantage to the industry. (8.3)

The collaborative club principle should be established to promote such research. (8.8)

8.	**Funding**	(a) R&D funding amounts to only 0.65% of UK construction output. Apart from manufacturers (55%), this is largely funded by the public sector which is also the client for 80% of civil engineering and 50% of all construction. The amount of funding in relation to output is less than for other major industries and much less than that of many of our major overseas competitors. (9.1)

If the findings of this report are to be implemented, the funding of R&D must increase substantially to the levels prevailing in our major international competitors. (9.1)

(b) There must be private industrial financial participation in R&D. However, private clients do not recognise the need to contribute, and contractors and consultants are limited in their financial capability. (9.6)

The construction industry should be encouraged to make a financial contribution to research principally through contributions to development work. Collaborative clubs should be promoted as one of the means of industrial involvement. (9.9)

(c) Contractors and consultants are typically agents who provide a service based on progress payments but, unlike other industries, they do not own the product. Consequently, their capital base profit and ability to contribute is small in relation to the turnover of the industry and the cost of its research needs. (9.2)

(d) The fruits of civil engineering research are generally in improved techniques which are not patentable and the benefits pass directly to the client. However, consultants and contractors benefit in improved capability in overseas markets. (9.1)

(e) The fragmentation of the industry into many small firms and labour-only contractors, places the R&D burden on a few large organisations. (9.2)

(f) It is concluded that public funding is the most appropriate to the structure of the industry, but used partly to generate private funds through collaborative programmes. A levy is seen as the only alternative but it is not recommended. (9.5)

The Government should recognise the need for the research process in the construction industry if the latter is to be an efficient industry at home and to be able to compete abroad. It should take steps to make the necessary money available, preferably by direct funding. (9.1)

9. **Role of the Institution** (a) A permanent research sub-committee is needed within the Institution to monitor and promote the construction research process and to liaise with and assist the proposed co-ordinating body. The needs revealed in this report require an active role by the Institution in fulfilling its role as a learned society. (10.7)

The Institution should have a permanent research sub-committee to promote and to monitor the research process. This sub-committee should publish a biennial report on progress. The Institution should formulate a research policy which takes into account the function of the proposed co-ordinating body. (10.7)

(b) The general lack of progress since the Task Force Report indicates that the Institution needs to take a major role in voicing the problems and in advocating solutions on a continuing basis. (10.6)

The Institution should publicise the problems of the construction research process and press Government to take the actions necessary to bring about a co-ordinating body and adequate levels of funding. (10.6)

(c) The Institution, through its Engineering Group Boards and their associated societies, has the organisation to stimulate members' interest and involvement in the research process, and to identify and promote research in most of the market sectors. The limitation on this major activity is lack of funding. (10.2)

The Institution should, within the funds available, through its Engineering Group Boards help to identify and promote research within the Boards' market sectors. It should also publish a 'Research Focus' at regular intervals on research progress in particular market sectors. (10.2 and 10.5)

(d) The chapter on Dissemination of Research Results has identified the needs for abstracting journals, research reviews, structured information, design manuals and the reporting of meritorious papers from elsewhere. Publications which separate researchers' and practitioners' interests tend to widen the communication gap between them. (10.3)

The Institution should review its Learned Society activities to take account of the recommendations on dissemination. (10.3)

(e) The need for a nationally accepted classification of status for published material has been identified so that users can gauge the degree of reliance they can place on published information. (10.3)

The Institution should endeavour to promote this proposal and support the proposed co-ordinating body in implementing it. (10.3)

10. **Review of research requirements** (Volume 2)

Reviews of the market sectors and discipline papers, prepared for the Task Force Report, were undertaken by invited specialists. The results were examined by the Engineering Group Boards and the findings were grouped under market sector headings. Findings related to management, safety and plant and equipment are also incorporated in Volume 2. Each market sector report contains views on the state of the market, recent developments and future needs. The final chapter of Volume 2 summarises the high priority R&D requirements identified in the market sector reports, presented, for ease of comparison, under the same discipline headings as were used in the Task Force Report.

The establishment of research priorities between market sectors and within market sectors is a continuing task which should be organised by a co-ordinating body. Resources should be made available so as to progress important subjects which have been identified.

ACKNOWLEDGEMENTS

The ICE Research Sub-Committee wishes to thank the following organisations and individuals for their help and co-operation in its work:

Association of Consulting Engineers
Balfours
Binnie & Partners
British Property Federation
Building Employers Confederation
Building Materials Producers Council
Building Research Establishment
Cement & Concrete Association
Chartered Institute of Building
Chartered Institution of Building Services Engineers
Construction Industry Research & Information Association
Department of the Environment
Engineering and Power Development Consultants Ltd
Federation of Association of Specialist Subcontractors
Federation of Civil Engineering Contractors
G. Maunsell & Partners
Hydraulics Research Limited, Wallingford
Institution of Structural Engineers
Kirk, McClure & Morton
Ministry of Agriculture, Fisheries and Food
National House Building Council
Natural Environment Research Council
NEDO Research Strategy Committee
Newcastle & Gateshead Water Company
Ove Arup & Partners
Peter Fraenkel & Partners
Rofe, Kennard & Lapworth
Royal Institute of British Architects
Royal Institute of Chartered Surveyors
Science and Engineering Research Council
SERC Environment Committee
Sir Alexander Gibb & Partners
Sir Robert McAlpine & Sons Ltd
Sir M. McDonald & Partners
Southern Water
Transport and Road Research Laboratory
Department of Civil Engineering, University of Bristol
Department of Civil Engineering, University of Dundee
Department of Civil Engineering and Building Science, University of Edinburgh
Department of Civil Engineering, University of Leeds
Department of Civil Engineering, University of Strathclyde
Water Research Centre
Watson Hawksley
W.S. Atkins Group Consultants
Energy Engineering Group Board
Engineering Management Group Board

Ground Engineering Group Board
Maritime Engineering Group Board
Safety in Civil Engineering Committee
Structural Engineering Group Board
Transportation Engineering Group Board
Water Engineering Group Board

P Ackers; Professor N N Ambraseys; Dr L C Archibald, Professor V Ashkenazi; Professor T Atkinson; P J Balfe; H C Balfour; J N Barber; R Barnsley; Dr S C C Bate; D Bayliss; A D M Bellis; Mrs M Bloom; J B Boden; M E Bramley; S Bratty; M A Brookes; Professor E T Brown; Professor F M Burdekin; W J Carlyle; P J Clark; K W Cole; Dr R D Coombe; J V Corney; R E Coxon; C Craig; R B Croft; D S Currie; F Dawson; D M Deaves; J A Derrington; R H R Douglas; G Duncan; J B L Faulkner, D Fiddes; D B Field; J B Field; Dr C A Fleming; Dr W G K Fleming; Professor G Fleming; I P Gillson; M A W Gooderham; H Goodman; K W Groves; G M Hannah; I W Hannah; M F Hardy; W Harvey; Dr N J Heaf; Professor A W Hendry; B A O Hewett; Dr G D Hobbs; Dr M W Holdgate; R W Horner; C Hotchkiss; R H Hughes; R B Johnson; D A Jolly; A H King; J R A Lang; P Lacey; Dr A S Laughton; E G Mabbs; G Margason; Professor D G McKinlay; G McQuire; Dr W L Mercer; C J Mettem; D W Miles; D S Miller; L Miller; J E Moore; E J Morley; C J E Morris; S N Mustow; Professor P Novak; T O'Brien; H R Oakley; H D Osborn; W Pemberton; J W Phillips; F F Poskitt; D W Quinion; Dr T M Ridley; A D Robb; D G M Roberts; B H Rofe; L Sallabank; Dr R H J Sellin; Dr T L Shaw; J K Smith; Dr S L Smith; P Stalker; E H Taylor; A Taylor; Professor P A Thompson; R L Thompson; S Thorburn; K Tomasin; Dr F Walley; B Wareham; Dr W L Wilkinson; A H Williams; T D Wilson; Dr L R Wootton; H L Yeadon.

GLOSSARY OF ABBREVIATIONS

ASCE	American Society of Civil Engineers
BCRA	British Ceramics Limited (formerly British Ceramics Research Association)
BILC	Building Industry Liaison Committee
BRAC	Building Regulation Advisory Committee
BRE	Building Research Establishment
BSI	British Standards Institution
BSRIA	Building Services Research & Information Association
BTG	British Technology Group (formerly NRDC)
CAD	Computer Aided Design
C&CA	Cement and Concrete Association
CAM	Computer Aided Manufacturing
CEGB	Central Electricity Generating Board
CHP	Combined Heat and Power
CIBSE	Chartered Institution of Building Services Engineers
CID	Construction Industry Directorate (DoE)
CIRIA	Construction Industry Research & Information Association
CITB	Contruction Industry Training Board
CONIAC	Construction Industry Advisory Committee
CPD	Continuing Professional Development
CRB	Construction Research Board
DEn	Department of Energy
DES	Department of Education and Science
DHSS	Department of Health and Social Services
DoE	Department of the Environment
DTI	Department of Trade and Industry
DTp	Department of Transport
EDCs	Economic Development Committees
FIDIC	Fédération Internationale des Ingénieurs Conseils
FIP	Fédération Internationale de la Précontrainte
GDP	Gross Domestic Product
HRL	Hydraulics Research Limited
HSE	Health and Safety Executive
IAEA	International Atomic Energy Agency
IPHE	Institution of Public Health Engineers
MAFF	Ministry of Agriculture, Fisheries and Food
MOD	Ministry of Defence
NEDO	National Economic Development Office
NERC	Natural Environment Research Council
NRDC	National Research Development Corporation
ODA	Overseas Development Administration
PFA	Pulverised Fuel Ash
PSA	Property Services Agency (DoE)
PWR	Pressurised Water Reactor
QA	Quality Assurance
RIBA	Royal Institute of British Architects
RSC	Research Strategy Committee (NEDO)
RWA	Regional Water Authorities
SERC	Science and Engineering Research Council
SPP	Specially Promoted Programme (SERC)

TRADA   Timber Research and Development Association
TRRL   Transport and Road Research Laboratory
UGC   University Grants Committee
WRc   Water Research Centre

BIBLIOGRAPHY

ADVISORY BOARD FOR THE RESEARCH COUNCILS. *Science and public expenditure 1986.* A Report to the Secretary of State for Education and Science for the Advisory Board for the Research Councils. 1986.

CONSTRUCTION INDUSTRY RESEARCH AND INFORMATION ASSOCIATION. *CIRIA: The first 25 years 1960-1985.* CIRIA, 1985.

DEPARTMENT OF THE ENVIRONMENT. *The balancing of interests between water protection and waste disposal.* DoE, 1976, Circular 39/76.

DEPARTMENT OF THE ENVIRONMENT. *Water research in the longer term.* DoE, 1986.

HAZARDOUS WASTE INSPECTORATE. *Second Report.* HMSO, 1986.

INSTITUTION OF CIVIL ENGINEERS. *Information provision for civil engineers – a pilot study.* ICE, April 1983.

INSTITUTION OF CIVIL ENGINEERS. *Research requirements in coastal engineering.* ICE, February 1985.

INSTITUTION OF CIVIL ENGINEERS. *Response to House of Lords Select Committee on Science and Technology.* ICE, March 1986.

INSTITUTION OF CIVIL ENGINEERS. *Response to the Building and Civil Engineering EDC's Report Strategy for Construction R&D.* ICE, March 1986.

INSTITUTION OF CIVIL ENGINEERS. *Second Report of the Infrastructure Planning Group.* ICE, March 1986.

NATIONAL ECONOMIC DEVELOPMENT OFFICE. *Strategy for construction R&D.* (Referred to as NEDO Report). NEDO, December 1985.

CIVIL ENGINEERING TASK FORCE. *Long-term research and development requirements in civil engineering.* (Referred to as Task Force Report). CIRIA, August 1981.

TAYLOR R.S. James Forrest Lecture. The influence of research and development on design and construction. *Proc. Instn Civ. Engrs,* Part 1, 1985, 78, June, 469-497.

WATER RESEARCH CENTRE. *Annual Review.* 1984-1985.

WATER RESEARCH CENTRE. *Research Programme.* 1985-1990.